Based on the book by Margaret Wise Brown

Pictures by Clement Hurd

SCHOLASTIC INC.
New York Toronto London Auckland
Sydney Mexico City New Delhi Hong Kong

GOODNIGHT MOON

ABC

An Alphabet Book

ISBN 978-0-545-40237-8

12 11 10 9 8 7 6 5 4 3 2 1   11 12 13 14 15 16/0

Printed in the U.S.A.   08

First Scholastic printing, September 2011

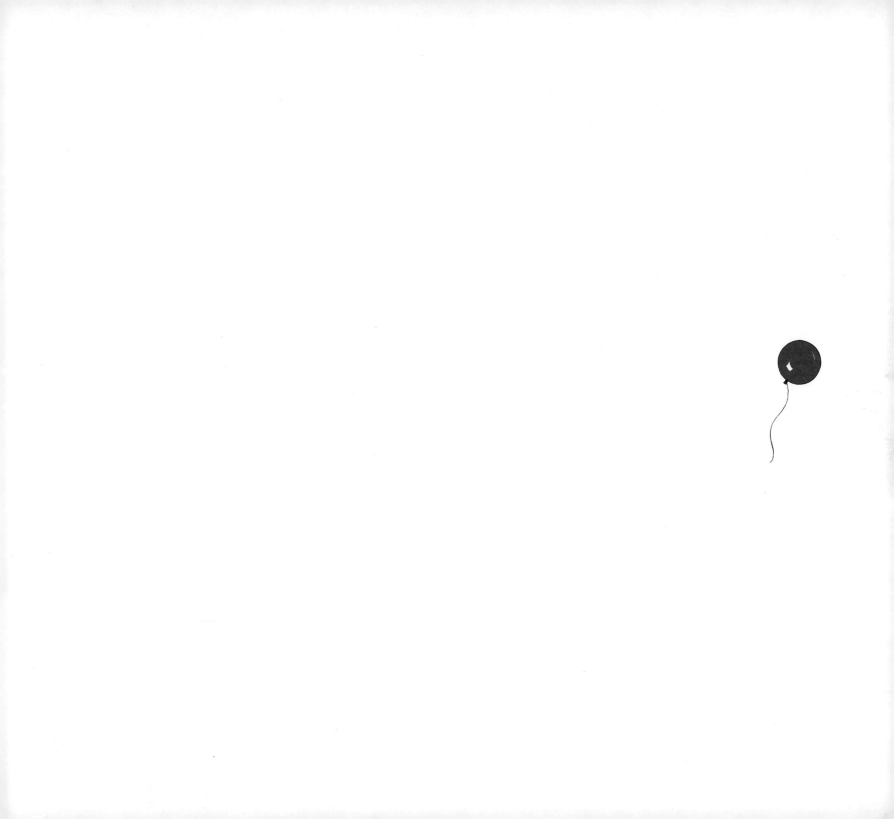

Aa Air

Bb Brush

Cc Clock

Dd Doll

Ee **Elephant**

Ff **Fireplace**

Gg **Giraffe**

Hh House

Ii In the great
green room

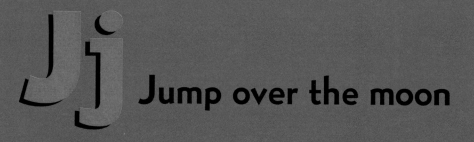

Jump over the moon

Kk Kittens

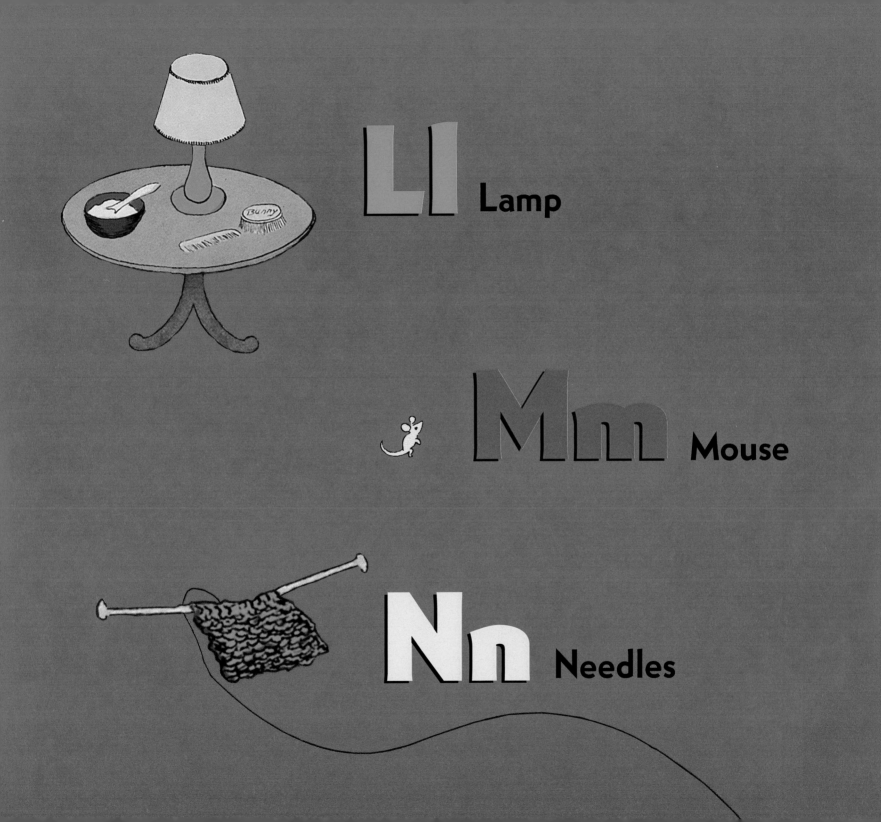

Ll Lamp

Mm Mouse

Nn Needles

Outside

Pp Paintings

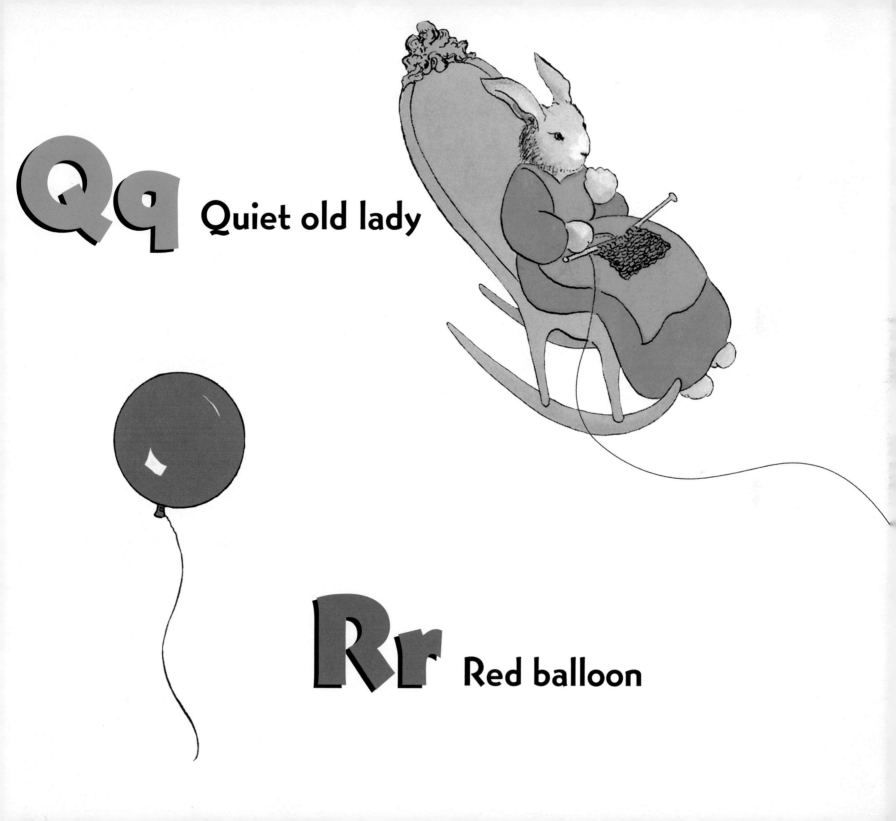

Qq Quiet old lady

Rr Red balloon

Ss Stars

Tt Telephone

Uu Under the covers

Vv Valley

Wood

Xx

Can you find me?

Yy Yarn

Goodnight stars

Goodnight air

Goodnight noises everywhere

Zz Zzzz . . .